The
Foul

Brown and Brown

Publishers: Brown and Brown,
               Keeper's Cottage,
               Westward,
               Wigton
               Cumbria CA7 8NQ
               Tel. 016973 42915

First published 2000

ISBN 1 870596 77 3

Printed by Reed's Ltd., Penrith, Cumbria on 100% recycled
paper and card.

Introduction

The Foul is a short story in five chapters about an incident at a soccer match. It is told by the two players involved, the referee and two rival supporters.

The Foul : Exercises, an accompanying book of photocopiable exercises, contains 4 pages of exercises for each chapter, and 10 pages of general exercises to be undertaken after reading the whole book. There are also suggestions for tutors on using the story for work on listening skills, for role play and for group discussion.

Please note: This book, **The Foul**, may not be photocopied.

Contents

1.

The Defender

It was a big match.

It was an end of season game.

We were ninth in Division 2.

If we won, we might get into the play-offs.

If we lost, we had no chance of going up.

We were 2 -1 up at the time.

There were only 20 minutes to go.

Their goalkeeper threw the ball to their No. 4.

He passed it to Dawson.

Dawson broke free with the ball.

There was just me between the goal and him.

He sent me the wrong way.

Then he went the other way.

I put out a leg for the ball.

I just touched it.

I was off balance.

My leg caught him below the knee.

He went down and rolled over twice.

He made it look a lot worse than it was.

It may have hurt him a bit.

But he was able to play on.

The ref. sent me off.

He gave me a red card.

It wasn't fair.

I hadn't been booked before in the match.

He could just have given me a yellow card.

Referees always pick on me.

They scored just before the end.

That draw cost us promotion.

The local press blamed me.

But the lads knew it wasn't my fault.

2.

The City Supporter

It was a big match.

It was near the end of the season.

We had to win to stay in Division 2.

We were fifth from bottom.

We were losing 2 - 1.

There were only 20 minutes left.

Dawson was going to score.

He sent Hooper the wrong way.

Dawson was almost past him.

He would have lobbed the goalkeeper.

Then Hooper brought him down.

I thought he had broken Dawson's leg.

It was a terrible foul.

He's always been a dirty player.

He once broke Garcia's leg in a Cup match.

Hooper got sent off for the foul on Dawson.

We should have had a penalty.

But the ref. was useless.

He only gave a free kick outside the box.

The foul was inside the box.

We could see that even from where we were, up the far end.

Dawson took the free-kick.

He was still limping a bit after the foul.

He put it over the bar.

Someone else should have taken it.

We got a second goal just before the end.

But we should have won the match.

In the end we did stay in the League.

But it went to the last game of the season.

3.

The United Supporter

It was a big match.

It was near the end of the season.

We had a chance to go up to Division 1.

We were ninth from the top.

There was only a couple of points between 4 clubs.

We were winning 2 - 1.

There were only 20 minutes left.

Their striker, Dawson, tried to get round Hooper.

Hooper's difficult to pass.

He's all arms and legs.

He got a foot to the ball.

Dawson dived and rolled into the penalty area.

He lay there, clutching his knee.

They all claimed a penalty.

Dawson made it look far worse than it was.

He'd never have scored anyway.

The ref. was useless.

He should have waved play on.

At the worst, it was a yellow card.

But he sent Hooper off.

We couldn't believe it.

Dawson had been kicking and pushing Hooper all day.

He always gets away with it.

He was the same when he played for Rangers.

Without Hooper, we had no chance.

They scored just before full-time.

That draw did for us.

We should have got into the play-offs.

We didn't get enough points from the last 4 games.

If Hooper hadn't been suspended, we would have got more.

Now we're still stuck in Division 2.

4.

The Striker

It was a big match.

It was one of the last games of the season.

We needed some points to stay in the League.

We were close to the relegation zone.

We were losing 2 - 1.

Hooper and I had been battling it out all afternoon.

We should have had a penalty in the first half.

Hooper held me down when we had a corner.

It would have been an easy header.

He's a hard tackler but I give as good as I get.

I got my own back on him just before half-time.

The foul happened halfway through the second half.

I got this great long ball from Jacko.

There was only Hooper to beat.

He's an awkward sod to get past.

He's not as quick as he used to be.

But he still isn't easy to beat.

I sent him the wrong way.

As I went past him, he brought me down.

He got me just below the knee.

It was deliberate.

He knew I was going to score.

He got sent off.

It was the first time the ref. had done the right thing all afternoon.

But he only gave us a free kick.

We should have had a penalty.

In the end, we managed to get a point.

It was what we had hoped for really.

We didn't expect to beat them away from home.

And we did stay up after all.

We got 5 points from the last three games.

At the end of the day, we avoided relegation by one point.

5.

The Referee

It was a big match.

It was near the end of the season.

Both teams needed the points.

United were close to the play-offs.

City were close to the relegation zone.

It wasn't as bad as some end of season games.

I booked a couple of City players in the first half.

That seemed to calm things down for a while.

Dawson and Hooper carried on having a go at each other.

I spoke to them as we went in at half-time.

The long ball to Dawson caught me out a bit.

I was on the edge of City's penalty area.

I had made it to the halfway line when
Hooper brought Dawson down.

He caught him on the knee.

The linesman flagged that it was outside
United's penalty area.

Dawson made a meal of it.

He always does.

He rolled about and clutched his leg as if it was broken.

He tried to claim that it was inside the penalty area.

I sent Hooper off.

It seemed the right thing at the time.

I saw it on local television a few days later.

It often looks a bit different on TV.

It was one of those tough decisions.

You have to make your mind up on the spot.

I wasn't in the perfect position.

But I did get a clear view of it.

The linesman said afterwards that he would have done the same.

Who would want to be a referee ?

Other readers with exercises

The Accident

Books *(set of 5):*
1. *The van driver's story*
   ISBN 1 870596 44 7
2. *The car driver's story*
   ISBN 1 870596 45 5
3. *The lorry driver's story*
   ISBN 1 870596 46 3
4. *The car passenger's story*
   ISBN 1 870596 47 1
5. *The policewoman's story*
   ISBN 1 870596 48 X

Exercises *ISBN 1 870596 49 8*

Alone in the Air

Book *ISBN 1 870596 71 4*
Exercises *ISBN 1 870596 72 2*

The Bank Raid

Book *ISBN 1 870596 67 6*
Exercises *ISBN 1 870596 68 4*

Chance of a Lifetime

Book *ISBN 1 870596 33 1*
Exercises *No ISBN*

Changing Partners

Book *ISBN 1 870596 64 1*
Exercises *ISBN 1 870596 65 X*

The Fire

Book *ISBN 1 870596 62 5*
Exercises *ISBN 1 870596 63 3*

A Place in the Sun

Book *ISBN 1 870596 75 7*
Exercises *ISBN 1 870596 76 5*

Shadow of a Doubt

Book *ISBN 1 870596 54 4*
Exercises *ISBN 1 870596 55 2*

Some Chance!

Book *ISBN 1 870596 52 8*
Exercises *ISBN 1 870596 53 6*

For a catalogue of publications, please contact:
Brown and Brown, Keeper's Cottage, Westward, Wigton,
Cumbria CA7 8NQ   *Tel. 016973 42915*